How to use this book

Follow the advice, in italics, given for you on each page.
Support the children as they read the text that is shaded in cream.
Praise *the children at every step!*

Detailed guidance is provided in the Read Write Inc. Phonics Handbook.

8 reading activities

Children:
- *Practise reading the speed sounds.*
- *Read the green, red and challenge words for the story.*
- *Listen as you read the introduction.*
- *Discuss the vocabulary check with you.*
- *Read the story.*
- *Re-read the story and discuss the 'questions to talk about'.*
- *Re-read the story with fluency and expression.*
- *Practise reading the speed words.*

Speed sounds

Consonants
Say the pure sounds (do not add 'uh').

f ff	l (ll)	m mm	n nn kn	r rr	s ss ce	v ve	z zz s	sh	th	(ng) nk

b bb	c k (ck)	d dd	g gg	h	j	p pp	qu	t tt	w wh	x	y	ch (tch)

Vowels
Say the vowel sound and then the word, eg 'a', 'at'.

at	hen head	in	on	up	day	see happy	high	blow

zoo	look	car	for	fair	whirl	shout	boy

*Each box contains one sound but sometimes more than one grapheme. Focus graphemes are **circled**.*

Green words

Read in Fred Talk (pure sounds).

r<u>igh</u>t   br<u>igh</u>t   ba<u>ck</u>   we<u>ll</u>   strip   must   ma<u>tch</u>   net   wi<u>ng</u>   pi<u>tch</u>

Read in syllables.

a' w<u>ay</u> → aw<u>ay</u>   be' gins → begins

Read the root word first and then with the ending.

s<u>igh</u> → s<u>igh</u>s   pl<u>ay</u> → pl<u>ay</u>ing

s<u>ay</u> → s<u>ay</u>s   pa<u>ss</u> → pa<u>ss</u>es

Red words

<u>the</u>   of   <u>are</u>   onto   <u>they</u>   we   he   to   g<u>oa</u>l*   ba<u>ll</u>*

* Red word for this book only

Vocabulary check

Discuss the meaning (as used in the story) after the children have read the word.

definition:

pitch   *a field for playing football on*

wing   *the side of the pitch*

goal   *scoring a point by getting the ball in the net*

strip   *sports clothes in team colours*

Punctuation to note in this story:

Jack Max	*Capital letters for names*
The They He	*Capital letters that start sentences*
.	*Full stop at the end of each sentence*
!	*Exclamation mark used to show surprise*
...	*Wait and see*

The big match

Introduction

Do you like playing football? Jack and Max love football and they play for a team called the Rays.

There's a big match between the Rays and the Jets and both teams really want to win the cup. Let's see what happens.

wheeee!

Story written by Cynthia Rider
Illustrated by Tim Archbold

It's the day of the big match.

The Rays are playing the Jets.

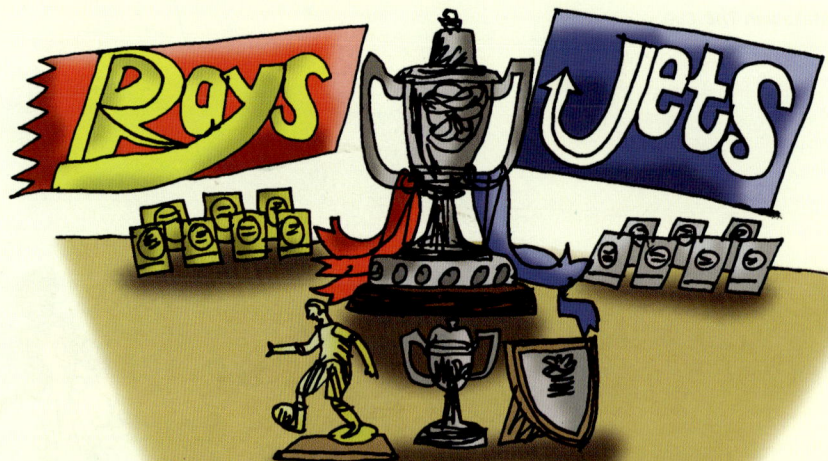

Jack puts on his bright red strip

and runs onto the pitch.

Wheeee ... the match begins.

The Rays play well. They get a goal right away.

But then they get a fright …

The Jets get

a goal as well!

Jack sighs.

"We must fight back or the Jets might win," he says.

Just then Max gets the ball.

He runs right up the wing

and passes it to Jack.

Jack kicks the ball high.

It lands in the net ...

and the Rays win the cup!

Questions to talk about

Re-read the page. Read the question to the children. Tell them whether it is a **FIND IT** *question or* **PROVE IT** *question.*

FIND IT

✓ Turn to the page

✓ Read the question

✓ Find the answer

PROVE IT

✓ Turn to the page

✓ Read the question

✓ Find your evidence

✓ Explain why

Page 8:   FIND IT   *What are the two teams called?*

Page 10:   FIND IT   *Who scores a goal first?*

                      FIND IT   *Why do the Rays get a fright?*

Page 12:   FIND IT   *Who passes the ball to Jack?*

Page 13:   PROVE IT   *What do you think Jack's team think of him?*